Quick &
Basic
Electricity

*A Contractor's Easy Guide to HVAC Circuits,
Controls, and Wiring Diagrams*

Quick &
Basic
Electricity

Carol Fey

P.I.G. Press
Littleton, Colorado

Disclaimer: This manual is intended as a tool for a classroom setting. Do not attempt any of the instructions in this book without the guidance of a qualified instructor.

Published by P.I.G. Press
759 E. Phillips Drive S.
Littleton, CO 80122-2873

Publisher's Cataloging-in-Publication Data
Fey, Carol.
    Quick & basic electricity: a contractor's easy guide to hvac circuits, controls & wiring diagrams / Carol Fey. — Littleton, CO: P.I.G. Press, 2000.
        p.   ill.   cm.
        ISBN 0-9672564-0-2
    1. Air conditioning—electrical equipment. 2. Heating—Equipment and supplies. 3. Electric wiring, interior.
        I. Title. II. Series.
TK4035.A35 .K57   2000   99-62710
697.9'3   dc—21   CIP

PROJECT COORDINATION BY JENKINS GROUP, INC.

03 02 01 00 ◆   5 4 3 2

Printed in the United States of America

*Dedicated to the many
heating and plumbing professionals
who have been good-humored "guinea pigs"
in my classes.*

Contents

Acknowledgments..*9*

How to Use This Book 11

Introduction 13

The Basic Circuit..17
    Power Supply 18
    Switches 26
    Loads..32

Series and Parallel Circuits....................................34
    Series Circuits 34
    Parallel Circuits...40

Meters 44
    Voltage...45
    Resistance 47
    Amperage 49

Relays 55

CONTENTS

Wiring Diagrams...61
    Hook-up/Connection/Schematic Diagrams..............61
    Ladder Diagrams...65
    Ladder and Hook-up Diagrams Together 70

Applying Your Knowledge 76

Index..79
Order Information 80

Acknowledgments

Thank you to Honeywell for providing the basic concepts for many of the drawings included in this book.

About the Author

Carol Fey is a degreed technical trainer who has worked in the controls industry for the last 20 years. She has been honored as National Technical Trainer of the Year by the American Society for Training and Development.

How To Use This Book

This book is for you if:

❖ You're intimidated about learning electricity.

❖ You've tried to learn electricity before and just didn't get it.

❖ You ought to know electricity, but don't want to ask for help.

❖ You fall asleep easily when in class or reading.

❖ When you have to read a book, it better be a short one.

This book is about basic electricity and low voltage controls electricity. It's about low voltage circuits, wiring, and reading wiring diagrams. It makes those things fun and easy—as they should be. The primary use for the information in this book is to understand basic electricity and controls for HVAC applications.

This book is not about house wiring,

The circuits and wiring samples presented here are

examples intended for learning. *You are cautioned not to actually do any wiring or work with electricity without the guidance of a qualified instructor or supervisor.*

This book is intentionally small. If you like, you can carry it with you and read it in small pieces. For many, that's the best way to learn. Or you can take it all in at once. It's short enough that it could be done in one sitting.

There's lots of white space. Go ahead and write in it with comments and questions. It's your book.

There are lots of pictures. You're encouraged to write on the pictures, too.

Have fun!

Introduction

Imagine that I just set a pink plush toy pig in front of you. It's battery powered. I ask, "What does this pig have to do with basic electricity?" I actually do this when I start out my basic electricity class. Then I hope and pray that some proud-to-be-mean-and-ugly guy growls, "Nuthin'!" Now we're cookin'.

I pick up the pig, switch it on, and set it back on the table. It begins to walk. It makes grunt, grunt noises. It's little tail quivers. The big mean guy crosses his arms over his chest in disgust. I'm in pig heaven.

"This pig has the same components as a basic electric circuit," I announce. "Does anyone have any idea what those are?—I'm looking for three of them." I get no response from anyone, of course. "In fact," I continue as I pull out my roll of pastel pig stickers, "I'm willing to give any of you a pig sticker for any answer. It doesn't even have to be a correct answer. See how easy this is!"

Sure enough, someone who can't resist the fun of this silliness, mumbles "It has a battery."

"Right!" I exclaim. "And a battery is a power supply. Both the pig and a basic electric circuit have a power supply." With considerable ceremony I award the sticker.

"OK," I continue, "what's another thing they have in common? C'mon," I say as I hold up the pig and point to the switch, "what's this thing that turns it on?"

"It's a switch," says someone who is willing to humor me. And I award another pig sticker.

I move on. "We have a power supply and a switch. What else do we need for a complete circuit? C'mon— what makes this pig move?"

From somewhere in the back I hear growled, "a motor."

"All right! A motor is a load. That's the third part. Now we have power supply, switch, and load. Who said motor?—you have a pig coming."

I don't hear anything, but I see a finger pointing to the big guy who'd earlier said "Nuthin'."

"Thank you, Sir, for your help," I say as I offer him his sticker. He won't take the sticker, but his buddy does. See, no one can resist P.I.G. Electricity!

Practical-Is-Good (that spells PIG) Electricity is different from every other basic electricity instruction you've ever had. Where else does electricity start with a pig, for one thing? And where else can you start out knowing nothing and get all the way to being able to work through an equipment diagram in just a few hours?

Basic electricity books and classes usually start pretty complex. It's not unusual for them to begin with electron theory (that's where they show you how the invisible plus and minus signs swim around inside wires). Electron theory!! What's that have to do with being able to wire or troubleshoot a circuit? "Nuthin'!" to quote the big mean ugly guy. So we're not going to do electron theory.

We're only going to think about the *practical* part of electricity. That means we're also not going to do math. There will be no Ohm's Law or Kirchoff's Law calculations (ah shucks!). There will be talk about the practical applications of these laws, though, so you'll learn what you need to know. But we won't let the stuff you don't need to know get in your way.

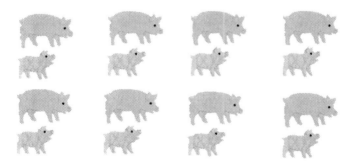

Just for the fun of it, and so that no one forgets that electricity is fun, imagine that a sheet of pig stickers came with this book. Go ahead, indulge yourself. Award yourself a sticker for just opening this book. Then be generous. Give yourself a sticker often.

Warning: Never experiment with electricity on your own or wire any circuit, including those in this book, without the presence of a qualified instructor or supervisor to assure your safety.

The Basic Circuit

Let's look closely at the battery-powered pig. The pig has the three basic components of a simple electrical circuit. Again these are power supply, switch, and load. Repeat—power supply, switch, and load. Every useful circuit has at least one of each of these. And just about everything in a circuit *is* one of these three.

The word *circuit* is related to the word *circle* (it's also related to circus, but never mind that). So take this moment to learn that a circuit must go in a complete circle. Try thinking of a circuit as a necklace. The three basic components are like beads. If they're all strung together without a break, it works.

Here's the basic circuit in a battery-powered pig.

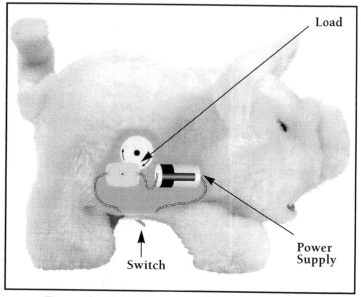

Figure 1. Basic circuit in a battery-powered pig.

Now let's look at each of components of the circuit, one at a time. Here's a reminder—the components of the circuit are power supply, switch and load.

Power Supply

Electricity must come from somewhere. In the pig, it's coming from a battery.

[Interesting but non-essential information: Battery power is called direct current, also known as DC. It's called direct current because on an oscilloscope (say "silly scope"), the pattern that direct current makes is a straight line (direct = straight)].

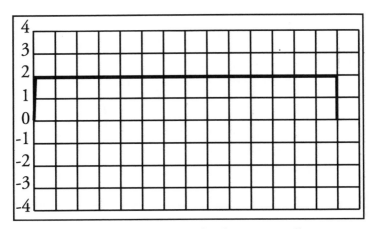

Figure 2. Direct current (DC) on an oscilloscope.

Often our circuits don't have batteries. We frequently plug into a wall outlet. Then the power supply is alternating current, also known as AC.

[More interesting but non-essential information: Alternating current is called *alternating* because on the oscilloscope it makes a pattern that alternates up and down. Never mind why it does that, it just does. Give yourself a pig sticker for wondering, though.]

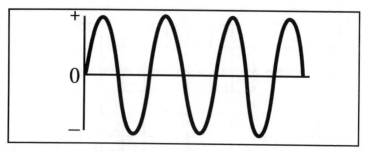

Figure 3. Alternating current (AC) on an oscilloscope.

Alternating current from the wall socket is often called line voltage, house current, or simply 120 (for 120 volts). It gets to the wall socket from the power plant through miles and miles of wire strung across the country.

My dad, an electric company electrician, explained it like this: The power plant makes *"really* big electricity" and sends it across power lines to a transformer. The transformer *transforms* or *steps down* really big electricity into smaller electricity. Even then it's still pretty big, so it's stepped down several more times before it comes into your house.

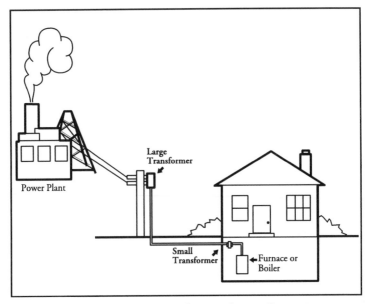

Figure 4. Power plant and transformers.

In an electrical diagram, the line voltage power supply is shown like this:

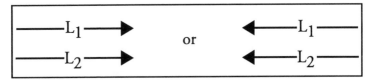

Figure 5. Symbols for line voltage power supply.

Learn to see the L1, L2, and two lines with arrows simply as the symbol for line voltage power supply.

For me there are two things about that symbol that bring up questions. First, if the rule is that a complete circuit can't have any breaks, how come there's a break between those two arrows? For an answer you get to use your imagination. Imagine that the circuit actually goes all the way back to the power plant where the electricity originates. Check out the picture below—you'll never see it this way anywhere else, but if it works. . . .

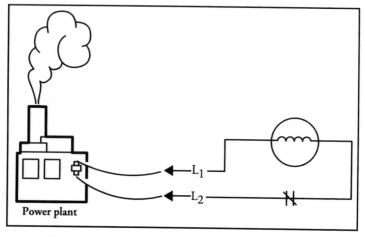

Figure 6. Line voltage circuit with power plant.

We're used to thinking that arrows point to the direction that something moves. In fact, it's tempting to want those arrows to show the direction that electricity is moving. Give up that idea. That's not what these arrows are doing. If you really need for them to be pointing to something, imagine they're both pointing to the power plant—the source of the electricity.

Once electricity is inside the house, it can either be used as 120V or it can be stepped down even further into what we call *low voltage.* Low voltage is 24V. We use 24V for most heating and air conditioning controls.

[Interesting but non-essential information: There are several reasons for using 24V for controls (thanks for asking, have a sticker!). One is that you don't have to be a licensed electrician to legally wire it. Second, low voltage allows us more accuracy for temperature control. Low voltage controls let us keep room temperature within a couple degrees of temperature setpoint. It's been found that most people can't sense less than 2 degrees difference between the warmest that the room gets and the coolest. Line voltage controls give more of a temperature difference (called temperature swing). When room temperature varies more than two degrees, people will say things such as "My, it's getting warm in here," or "Crank up the heat, would ya."]

Never forget that when dealing with heating and air conditioning, we're in the *comfort* business.

The step down transformer we use to take 120V down to 24V looks like this:

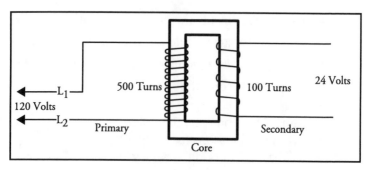

Figure 7. Step down transformer.

A transformer has two sides. The *primary* (just like in school, primary means first) side is often shown on the left side. It's where the electricity first comes in. The primary is typically 120V. The voltage is going *into* the transformer.

The right side of the drawing shows the *secondary*. This shows the electricity after it's been stepped down. This side is typically 24V. This voltage is coming OUT of the transformer. The secondary side of the transformer is the power supply for a 24V circuit.

The chunk of iron in the middle of the transformer is called the core. Transformers are one of the few things left where heavier still is better. Heavier means more iron, and more iron insures reliable transfer of voltage from the primary to the secondary.

[Interesting but non-essential information: If you're wondering how primary voltage gets transformed to secondary voltage, the simple explanation is *magic*. A more useful explanation is electromagnetism.]

Somewhere back in elementary school you may have had a science lesson where you learned you could wind a wire around a big nail, power the wire, and turn the nail into a magnet. The primary side of the transformer is like that wire, and the core is like that nail.

We call that wire wound around the core the *primary winding*.

On the secondary side of the transformer we find a completely separate winding. We call it the secondary winding. The primary and secondary windings do not connect to each other. There is no physical or electrical connection between them. The only relationship between the primary and secondary is magnetic.

Look at the transformer drawing again. On the left side is the primary at 120V. On the right side is the secondary at 24V. The drawing says there are 500 *turns* or *windings* of the primary wire around the primary side of the core. And the drawing tells us that there are 100 turns on the secondary side. The relationship between 500 turns and 100 turns is 5 to 1. Or, there are 1/5 as many windings on the secondary as the primary. So we could expect there to be 1/5 as much voltage on the secondary as the primary. It works—1/5 of 120V is 24V, just what we were looking for.

For the record, transformers can also be *step up*.

In a wiring diagram, the low voltage power supply is shown like this:

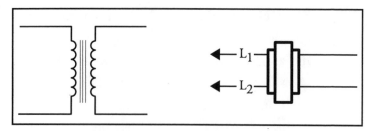

Figure 8. Transformer symbols.

Switches

Everyone is used to the idea that you turn something on and off with a switch.

What's not so familiar is thinking that when a switch is on, the switch is also closed. And when a switch is off, the switch is open.

Let's look inside a simple switch.

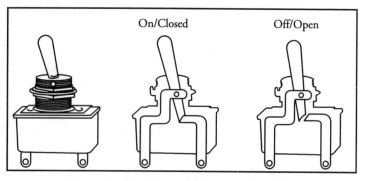

Figure 9. Simple switch, closed and open.

Here are two sets of symbols for open and closed switches:

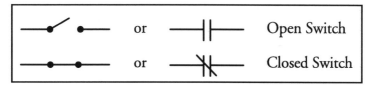

Figure 10. Switch symbols.

Remember the basic circuit and how it has to be a complete (closed) circle in order to work. If there is an *open*ing it doesn't work. The switch simply does the closing and the opening of the circuit.

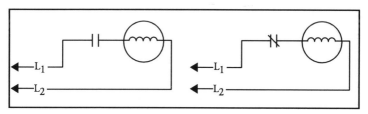

Figure 11. Open circuit and closed circuit.

Note to plumbers. The comparison of electricity to water works only so far. Here's where it stops working. When a valve is open, stuff flows through it. When a valve is closed, stuff stops. But in an electrical circuit, open means there is a break in the electricity's path—an open switch is *off*.

[Interesting but non-essential information: Switches are sometimes identified with four letters, for example SPST or DPDT. S stands for *single*, D for *double*, P for *pole*, and T for *throw*. You already understand single and double.

A *pole* in a switch is where two points connect. Think of a fishing pole. If you hold one end and your buddy holds the other, you have a single pole. If you have two more buddies standing beside the first two of you, and a separate pole connects them, you have *double pole(s)*. There is no electrical connection between the two poles. But in switches, the two poles have to connect or disconnect at the same time.

Keep thinking about fishing (when did someone last tell you that?). Imagine it's just you this time holding a pole. If you cast, or throw, so that the pole connects you and your buddy, that's *single throw*. If you could also cast behind and connect with another buddy, you would have *double throw*. You can connect with one buddy or the other, not both.

If you have a double *pole*, you can now see that your *throws* could be either *single* throw or *double* throw.]

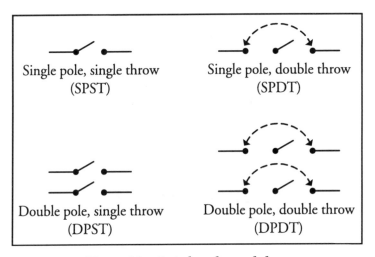

Figure 12. Switch poles and throws.

A thermostat is just a switch

A thermostat is just a switch. Aquastats and humidistats are switches. In the world of heating and air conditioning controls, anything with *stat* as part of its name is a switch. A *thermo*stat is for room temperature, an *aqua*stat is for water temperature, and a *humidi*stat is for humidity. Each of these stats opens or closes in reaction to a particular condition.

A heating thermostat closes its switch when the temperature drops to a certain point. This brings on the heat. The same switch opens when there is enough heat, which turns the heat off.

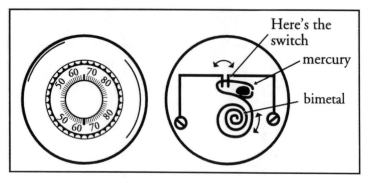

Figure 13. A thermostat is a switch.

[Interesting but non-essential information:
No matter the brand of thermostat, a good
quality non-electronic low voltage thermostat will be a mercury bulb switch.
Mercury is used because of its unique property of
being a metal and a liquid. It conducts electricity and
it moves easily.

Look again at the thermostat drawing. What would it
take for the mercury inside the bulb to flow to where
it would connect the two terminals of the switch? If
the bulb would tip toward the left, the mercury would
flow to the switch, right?

And what would cause that tipping action?
Connected to the bulb is a coil of metal called a
bimetal. You know that metal expands when it is
heated and contracts when it is cooled. If the bimetal cooled (as in "it's getting cold in here"), it would
contract. Look at the drawing and notice that if the
bimetal contracts, the mercury bulb is tipped to the
left. That's just where we need it to be to have the
mercury in a position to connect the two terminals of
the switch. Voila, the heat is on!]

[Interesting but non-essential information: Switches that control temperature (e.g. thermostats, aquastats) are designed to open or close on either temperature rise or temperature fall. A heating thermostat, for example, closes on temperature fall (the switch turns on as the room temperature falls). A high limit safety switch (aquastat or fan and limit switch) opens on temperature rise (the switch turns off as the system temperature gets too high). Switching action is particularly important when selecting replacement controls.]

There are endless varieties of switch symbols. Don't let yourself be distracted by all the little details added to the basic symbols. A switch is still a switch. For our work here it's either open or closed, no matter how or why it got that way. A fuse is a one-time switch.

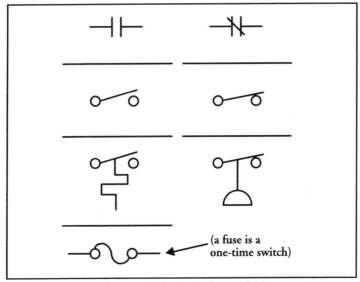

Figure 14. Switch symbols.

Loads

A user of electricity is called a load. A load typically uses electricity to create heat, motion, light, sound, etc. Examples of loads are motors, light bulbs, and doorbells.

The symbol for a load in a wiring diagram almost always appears as some kind of squiggle. The squiggle shows that the load offers resistance— it won't be easy for electricity to get through it. And the resistance is what causes the heat, light etc.

The motor symbol is an exception to a load always having a squiggle. When you see the symbol, just use your imagination and connect the two dots with a squiggle.

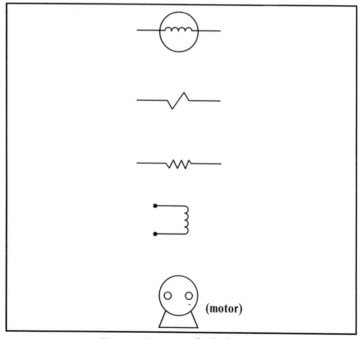

Figure 15. Symbols for loads.

Note about grounding: Individual 24V circuits do not normally need to be grounded. It is the responsibility of the licensed electrician who brings in line voltage to assure that the grounding is correct for the building. Grounding is of concern in controls circuits when we work with millivoltage, such as with electronic ignition. In the case of electronic ignition, the voltage is so small that we ground the circuit to the furnace to make sure that the voltage makes it all the way through the circuit. This is the same principle as applies to the electrician providing "earth ground," but it is a somewhat different application.

Series and Parallel Circuits

To review, a circuit consists of a power supply, a switch, and a load. The way that we wire these components together determines what the circuit will do. For our purposes here, we'll look at two kinds of circuit: series and parallel. We can build each with exactly the same components, but the results will be quite different. It is not a case of series or parallel being better than one another. Which one we use depends on what we're trying to do.

Series circuits

Series always means stringing things together in a row, one after the other. For example, we speak of the World Series, which is a string of ball games. Pre-1990s Christmas tree lights have all the bulbs (loads) strung in a series. When one bulb goes bad, all the lights go out. If you're like me, at one time or other you've sat under that tree replacing one light at a time, only to find out hours later that there were two bad bulbs!

Here's a diagram of a series circuit.

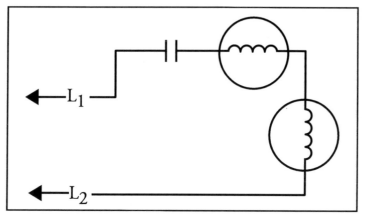

Figure 16. A series circuit diagram.

Trace this circuit with your finger or a pencil. It doesn't matter which direction you go. Notice that the electricity has to go through the first load before it gets to the second. If electricity can't get through the first load (imagine the coil broken, as in a burned out light bulb—rattle, rattle, that's the broken coil), it can't get to the second. The break in a load is an opening in the circuit (in fact we even call it an open). It has the same effect as an open (off) switch or a disconnected wire.

If it seems to you that loads ought to be powered along the circuit as far as the electricity gets before the break. . . forget that idea, it just doesn't work that way. The electricity has to get all around the circuit and back to the beginning before anything will happen.

In a series circuit, either both loads are on or both are off.

Imagine a hands-on demo board. (I am not suggesting that you actually do this.) If we were in class, I would have you wire up a series circuit using two household light bulbs and a switch. You would see what you already know—that turning on the switch turns on both bulbs. And you would see that unscrewing either bulb causes both bulbs to go out.

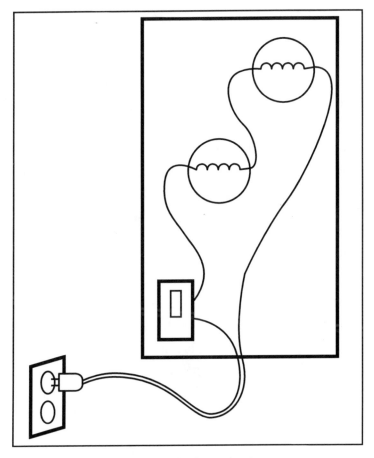

Figure 17. Series wiring.

Kirchoff's Law

You expected what you've seen so far. But here's something that may surprise you. These are 60 watt bulbs on our imaginary demo board, but they look only half-bright enough. The explanation is given in a formula called

Kirchoff's Law. (Don't worry, we're not going to do math.) Kirchoff's Law tells us that in a series circuit, the available voltage has to be divided among all the loads. Like dinner time with too many kids, nobody gets as much as they want.

In the case where there are two loads of equal wattage (think of wattage for a moment as appetite), each load gets half of what he wants. So the bulbs really are half as bright as it seems they ought to be. (Don't confuse watts with volts here. It's purely coincidental that 60 watts plus 60 watts— 120 watts—is the same number as the voltage of the circuit.)

In your imagination, replace those two light bulbs with two motors. If you wired two motors in series, you couldn't expect either of them to run right. Right?

Let's take this a little farther and play a guessing game. You now know that two equal bulbs each get half. What happens with unequal loads? Let's replace one of those bulbs with a 25W bulb, so we have one 60W and one 25W. What's your guess?

Here are the choices:

    a. The 60W looks like a 60W and the 25W looks like a 25W

    b. The bulbs look identical

    c. The 60W is brighter because the big guy always wins

    d. The 25W is brighter because the little guy gives less resistance

And the answer is: (d) the little guy wins because he offers less resistance! Give yourself a pig sticker no matter what answer you chose. As they say, both kids and electricity take the path of least resistance.

Back to the imaginary demo board, if we were in class, it would appear that the 25W bulb is fully bright and that the 60W bulb isn't lighted at all. But from what you already know, in a series circuit either both loads are on or both are off. That means that if the 25W bulb is lighted the 60W bulb must be lighted too.

Let's check a little closer. When you cup your hand around the 60W that seems to be off, you can feel heat, and you can see a bit of light. Testing a little further, if you unscrew the 60W bulb, the 25W goes out as well.

It's tempting right now to believe that series circuits are useless. That may be the case when we put loads in series. But switches in series are very useful. Let's look at that possibility.

Unlike loads, we find it useful for one switch to be able to control the whole circuit. A safety switch is a good example of it being good for one switch to be able to call off the whole deal.

It's quite common in controls circuits to have two or more switches in series. Think for a minute about how we use switches in control circuits. Many of them are safety switches of one kind or another such as a high limit switch or flame rollout switch. In a furnace or boiler, each safety switch is guarding for one particular unsafe condition.

Since all safety conditions must be met for safe operation, all the switches in the string of switches must be closed. These switches are normally closed, and open only if there is an unsafe condition.

The figure below shows three switches in series. All are normally closed. Suddenly one control senses an unsafe situation and opens.

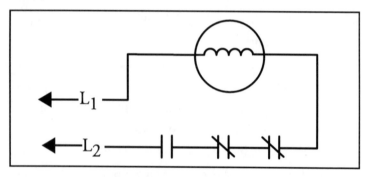

Figure 18. Switches in series.

Would we want to keep the equipment in operation until all three switches sensed separate unsafe situations? Not in my house!

Parallel circuits

Using the same components as we used in the series circuit—a power supply, a switch and two loads—let's wire a parallel circuit this time.

40

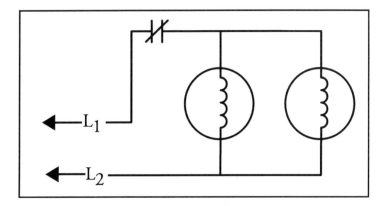

Figure 19. Parallel circuit.

Take a moment to assure yourself that the components are the same, even though the drawing looks quite different. We'll soon see that they perform very differently, too.

The easiest way to look at a parallel circuit is this: each load is in its own circuit with the power supply and the switch. Notice that if we block out one load, the other load remains in a complete circuit.

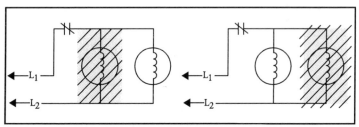

Figure 20. Parallel circuit, load 1 removed, then load 2 removed.

Let's return to the imaginary hands-on demo. This time we'll picture wiring it as a parallel circuit.

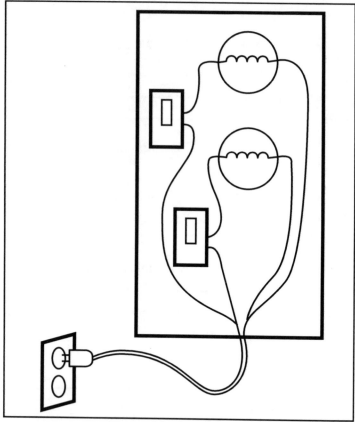

Figure 21. Parallel wiring.

If you hypothetically powered this circuit, you would see that both 60W bulbs are fully bright. You'd also notice that if you unscrewed one bulb, the other remained lit. A parallel circuit certainly simplifies life with loads, doesn't it?

Here's something to think about. In many bathrooms you've seen a strip of four light bulbs above the sink. What do you think—are they in series or in parallel? Hint: recall that you can wait until most of the bulbs are burned out before have to replace any. Is your answer different than you would have given before you learned about circuits?

We have one more thing to check out. Imagine our classroom demo board and replace one of the 60W bulbs with a 25W. Would you imagine the bulbs to look like they're *supposed* to look, or would you expect something tricky like we saw with the series circuit? Right-o! Life is pretty much what we expect when we wire loads in parallel.

Meters

Sometimes we need to use a meter to find out what's going on in a circuit. I know there are plenty of old timers who size up a circuit by how hard it sets them on their tail. But go ahead, be a wimp—use a meter. If nothing else, it'll save you a lot of time.

A meter is called a *multi*meter because it has multiple functions. With one meter you can usually measure volts, amps and ohms. You can measure each of these three for alternating current (AC) or direct current (DC). That gives six possible functions. It's up to you to select the function you need.

	Voltage (V)	Amperage (A)	Resistance (Ω)
AC	x	x	x
DC	x	x	x

In controls circuits we use primarily AC, so let's limit our selections to alternating current functions. These functions will be marked either AC or with the little AC squiggle (∼).

Voltage

Voltage is indicated by the letter V. The alternating current voltage function is marked either *VAC* (doesn't stand for vacation, vacuum or vacant) or the letter V with a squiggle (∼) for AC over it. We call the voltage part of the meter a *volt*meter. While you're choosing meter functions, you also need to select the highest voltage measurement that you could possibly find. That's so you don't damage the meter.

The most common use of voltage measurement in controls work is to find out if you have any. Some guys use their finger or tongue—you have more class (and sense) than that.

Let's go to our imaginary hands-on demo board. Let's say we want to know if there is power to the circuit. We can expect any incoming voltage to be around 120V, so you would set your meter accordingly.

On your meter you'll find two *leads* or *probes*. One is black and one is red. For our purposes here, it doesn't matter which you put where.

To check for voltage coming into the circuit, put one lead on L1 and one on L2.

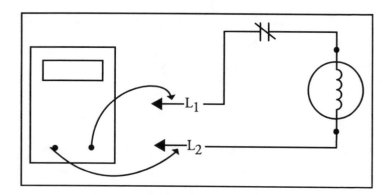

Figure 22. Using a voltmeter to check for voltage.

You would see a meter reading a few tenths above or below 120V. But the purpose of this step was to find out if there was any voltage at all. If there is, you can say, "Yep, we got power."

[Interesting but non-essential information: the voltage delivered by the utility can vary depending on time of day or time of year or location. When there is a greater overall demand by consumers (e.g. during extremely hot weather), your voltage may be lower.

Keep in mind as the voltage going into your transformer primary side goes up or down, so does the voltage coming from your transformer secondary.]

The next most common use of the voltmeter is to find out how much voltage you have.

For example, you'll occasionally find on a diagram an indication such as "24VAC nom."

This means that for the control to work it has to have a nominal (minimum) 24V. In this case you'd use the voltmeter to make certain the voltage is at least 24V.

Take a moment to notice that positioning the meter this way puts it in a parallel circuit with the load.

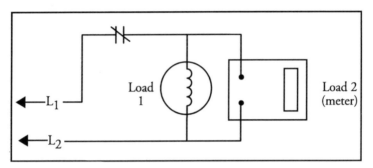

Figure 23. Using a voltmeter (parallel with the load).

Resistance

Perhaps you've watched your buddies take their meter from the case, turn a dial, and make it squeal or beep. Beyond being annoying, there's no reason to do this at this point. But here's what's going on. When the "ohmmeter" function is selected, you can cause the beep by touching the two probes together. The beep is the meter's way of saying, "I found an unbroken path to send out electricity and get it back.

Resistance is indicated by the Greek letter omega (Ω). It looks like an upside-down horseshoe. That symbol is used because the measurement is ohms, but to use the letter "O" would look too much like a zero.

When you touch the two meter probes together the path is simply from one probe to the other—big deal. But imagine how useful it could be to find out if there is an unbroken path through a load such as a motor coil or a light bulb. You would touch one probe to each side of the load. If the meter beeps, it has found an unbroken path. That means the load (e.g. the motor coil or the light bulb element) is good. This is particularly useful when you can't see what's going on inside.

We might also use a process called a *continuity check*, to see if a wire inside insulation is continuous or if it is broken.

Additionally, we could use the ohmmeter to find out if a switch is open or closed by checking it for continuity. Put a probe on each side of the switch. If the meter beeps, there is an uninterrupted path through the switch—the switch is closed. If there is no sound, the switch is open.

When we did these continuity checks the meter was looking for resistance to the flow of electricity. Along with the beep, the meter gave a numerical reading on its display. This reading is the amount of resistance it found, measured in *ohms*. For basic controls work we don't pay much attention to this reading. We're looking for the beep or no-beep.

When the multimeter is in ohmmeter function, the battery in the meter becomes the power supply. Because of this it's important for you to remove or turn off any other power to the circuit. You don't need to select AC or DC because the meter is supplying the power. See the diagram below for the power supply-switch-load configuration when using the ohmmeter.

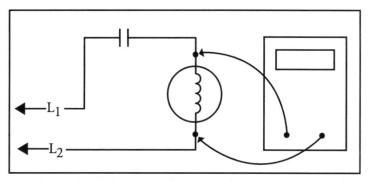

Figure 24. Using an ohmmeter (remove power first).

Amperage

The final meter function is that of an ammeter. You won't find this function on the more inexpensive meters. An ammeter measures amperes, or amps. Amps are abbreviated as "A".

Every load has an *amp rating*. It is often called *amp draw.* You can find the amp rating printed on a load, on its box, and in the product data sheet. Finding the amp draw of a circuit is as simple as adding the amp ratings of all the loads.

But if you're not sure that you've identified all the loads in the circuit, you can use the ammeter to measure the amp draw of the entire circuit. In controls work the amp draw will often be in tenths of an amp, so you will need to use a digital meter that measures in decimals.

An ammeter must be placed in series in the circuit. That means you must break the circuit and put the ammeter in it.

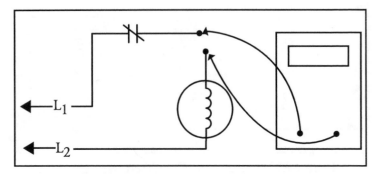

Figure 25. Using an ammeter (in series with the load).

Sometimes the easy way to get the ammeter in series is to place the probes on the terminals of a switch, such as the thermostat. The ammeter there will have the effect of closing the switch.

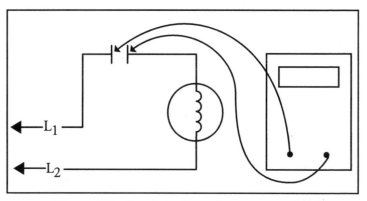

Figure 26. Ammeter in series across a switch.

If you have a meter with a clamp attachment, the easiest way of all to measure the amp draw is to clamp around any wire in the circuit.

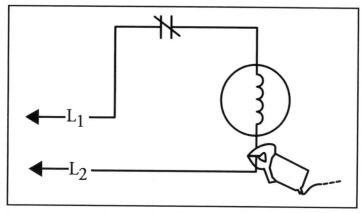

Figure 27. Clamp-on ammeter.

When you measure amps, the loads must be powered for a minute or so before you get an accurate reading.

There are two important uses for amp measurement in controls circuits.

One use for amp measurement is to make sure you don't overload the transformer. If you do overload the transformer, you can easily pull too much amperage through its secondary side. That's called burning or smoking the transformer.

A transformer has a *VA rating*. VA means volts times amps. A 40VA transformer is typical in a controls circuit. This means that the circuit's total amps multiplied by 24V (a given) must not exceed 40 VA. If it does exceed you must either remove a load or replace the transformer with one of a higher VA rating.

Cycle rate

Another use for the circuit's amp draw is to set the thermostat's cycle rate. Cycle rate is the number of times per hour that the heating or air conditioning equipment can come on if it is needed. Six cycles per hour (every ten minutes) is the industry standard for forced air and hydronics in order to assure maximum comfort.. You get this six cycles per hour when you set the thermostat anticipator to match the amp draw of the controls circuit.

Here's a quick review for setting the anticipator: Set your digital meter for AC amps. Place one probe on thermostat terminal R and one probe on terminal W. The heat will come on. Let the equipment run for a minute or so, or until the meter reading stabilizes. Set the anticipator for that reading. (Note: on new installations, the equipment manufacturer will usually tell you the desired anticipator setting.)

[Interesting but non-essential information: Most people are not aware of a temperature swing of less than two degrees. It has been found that this two-degree range is best maintained by giving the heating a chance to come on every 10 minutes (60 minutes divided by six cycles per hour = 10-minute cycles). In error some folks think that they might save money by running their gas furnace less often—maybe only every 20 minutes. But look at the chart of how temperature swings increase as we decrease from 6 cph to 3 cph.]

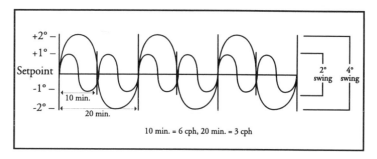

Figure 28. Cycle rates and temperature swing.

A cycle is on-time plus off-time. When there is little demand for heat, the equipment will run only a short part of that ten-minute cycle. If there is no need for heat, it won't run at all that cycle. When there is a great demand for heat (baby, it's cold outside), the equipment will run a greater portion of that cycle. If necessary, it could run all the way through one cycle and continue into the next.

For various reasons, we may want to use a cycle rate other than 6 cph. Equipment manufacturers specify cycle rate for new installations. High efficiency gas furnaces are often specified for 3 cph. For hydronics with heavy cast iron radiators, 3 cph is often advised. (This doesn't apply to baseboard hydronics—leave that at 6 cph.) It's often advised to use 9 cph for electric heat.

Electronic thermostats come with a cycle rate adjustment. You just select the one you want.

You can change the cycle rate on non-electronic thermostats by adjusting the anticipator setting. For 3 cph, simply multiply the circuit's amp draw by 1.8 and set the anticipator to that number. For 9 cph, multiply by .8.

Relays

A circuit can have only one voltage. With that in mind, consider how we might manage to control line voltage equipment with low voltage controls. Low voltage controls provide greater comfort, but equipment such as blower motors, compressors, and circulators are usually line (120) voltage. How are we going to do this?

The most common way to let unlike voltage devices work together is through a relay. Think of a relay as a translator. If I can speak only Greek and you can speak only English, we need a translator who can speak both languages. If the thermostat is 24V and the motor is 120V we need a relay—which can deal with both. Hold onto that thought.

A relay consists of two parts: a coil and a switch (or several switches).

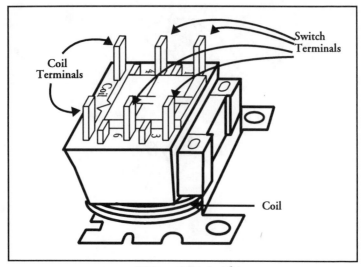

Figure 29. A relay.

In a diagram the coil is often labeled *1K*. The switches would be labeled 1K1, 1K2 etc. If there were additional relays in the same system, the second relay coil would be labeled 2K. The switches associated with coil 2K would be labeled 2K1, 2K2, etc. Note that 1K2 and 2K1 are not the same.

Occasionally a different labeling system is used. The labels could be as straightforward as *relay coil* and *relay switch*.

Each part of the relay is in a different circuit. Because there is no electrical connection between the relay parts, each circuit's voltage can be different. We'll talk about the connection below.

The relay coil, like any coil, is always a load. The switches, of course, function as switches.

Let's look at just the 24V coil circuit (dotted line part of the diagram below). The coil is the load. A thermostat is the switch. Since it's a 24V circuit, the power supply is the 24V side (or secondary side) of the transformer.

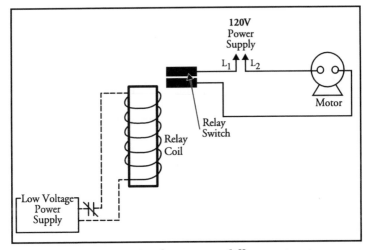

Figure 30. A relay in two different circuits.

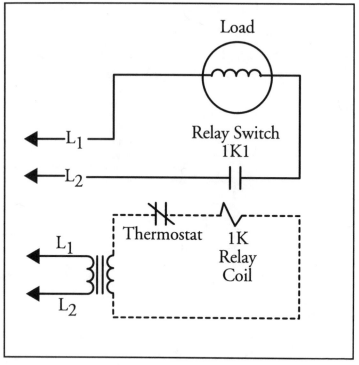

Figure 31. Relay circuits.

When the thermostat switch closes, it allows power to flow through the relay coil. We now say that the relay coil is powered. When the coil is powered, it creates electro-magnetism. The magnetism causes the relay switches to change position. If the switches are open, they close. If they are closed, they open. There can be some of each.

Now let's look at a relay switch circuit (solid line part of the above relay diagram).

The load in this circuit is a 120V motor, the switch is the relay switch, and the power supply is 120V line voltage.

The motor probably is part of a piece of heating and air conditioning equipment.

Let's review the above chain of events where the 24V thermostat turns on the relay, which turns on the 120V motor. In the 24V circuit the thermostat switch closes. That allows the relay coil to be powered with 24V from the secondary side of the transformer. As soon as the relay coil is powered, it creates magnetism that causes any switches inside the relay to change position. There is probably more than one switch. But the one we're looking at moves from open to closed because of the magnetism from the coil. The closing of that relay switch allows120V to flow from the line voltage power supply to the motor. The motor is now on.

Here's some more information about relay switches. Relay switches are referred to as *normally open* (N.O.) or *normally closed* (N.C). *Normally* means when the coil is not powered. The switches (and there usually are more than one) on the top of the relay might be labeled either N.O. or N.C. Or they may be labeled with the symbols you saw in the section about switches.

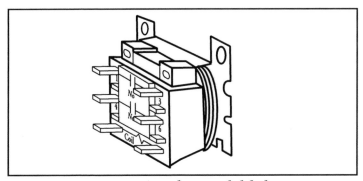

Figure 32. Relay switch labeling.

The tricky part about relays is remembering that as soon as the coil is powered, the switches are no longer in their *normal* position. When the relay is powered the switch position is the opposite of what the label says. That means that a normally open switch is closed. (We're not in Kansas any more, Toto!) Fortunately, that's usually what we're trying to accomplish anyway.

A relay in a wiring diagram often looks like this:

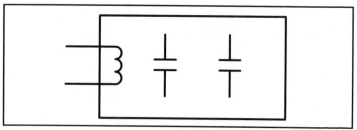

Figure 33. Relay symbol.

As we might expect, the coil looks like a coil and the switches are drawn as switches. Note that as soon as the coil is powered, both of these open switches become closed.

Wiring Diagrams

Hook-up/connection/schematic diagrams

We're going to put together some of the things you now know into a new wiring diagram.

This kind of diagram is called a *hook-up diagram,* a *connection diagram,* or a *schematic.* Regardless of the name, it shows how the circuit is wired.

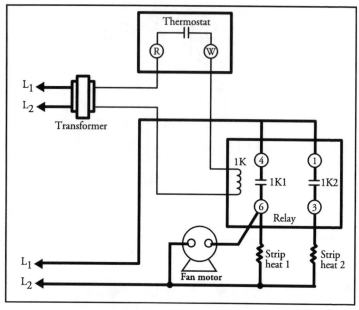

Figure 34. A basic hook-up, connection, or schematic wiring diagram.

Here are a couple new things to note:

  ❖ a heavy line is used for line voltage; a light line is used for low voltage.

  ❖ the line voltage power supply (L1/L2) may be shown more than once. The power is all coming from the same place (the power plant, right?)

Let's begin looking at the diagram on the upper left side. We find line voltage (heavy lines) going into the primary side of the transformer. And we find low voltage (light lines) coming out from the secondary side of the transformer.

With your finger or a pencil, trace the light line up to the thermostat. So far, we have the transformer secondary as the 24V power supply and the thermostat as the switch. With your pencil mark that thermostat switch closed. (In real life, a call for heat would close the thermostat switch.)

Continue tracing the 24V circuit to the coil of the relay. Because the thermostat switch is closed, there is power to this coil. Continue tracing the low voltage circuit back to the transformer secondary. We have a complete circuit. The load (the relay coil) is now powered.

[Interesting but non-essential information: R and W are conventional thermostat terminal designations. The R terminal is to be connected to the power supply (transformer secondary side) and the W terminal is to be connected to the load. The wire to R is typically red and the wire to W is typically white.]

Now remember back just a page or two to relay switches. Because they are drawn open, these relay switches are "normally open." What happens when we power a relay coil? Yes, both of those N.O. switches close when the coil is powered. With your pencil mark these two relay switches closed.

Now we're ready to look at the line voltage circuit. That's the heavy lines.

At the bottom left of the diagram, find the line voltage power supply (L1/L2 and the two arrows). Trace the heavy line to the right, up and over to the first relay switch. That switch is labeled with both 1K1 and terminals 4 – 6.

Remember that we closed that switch when we powered coil 1K.

As soon as we get through switch 1K1 we have a choice of tracing through the fan motor or the strip heat 1. Let's go through the fan motor, and trace back to the power supply. We have a complete circuit. The motor is powered.

Let's trace another circuit from the line voltage power supply. Trace the same direction as before, through the same (closed) switch. This time, instead of going through the fan motor, trace through the load labeled strip heat 1. Continue back to the power supply. We have another complete circuit. Strip heat 1 is powered.

For a third time begin at the line voltage power supply and trace a circuit, this time through switch 1K2, also labeled terminals 1 - 3. Switch 1K2 is closed because coil 1K is powered. Trace through this closed switch, through the load labeled strip heat 2 and back to the power supply. We have a third complete circuit. Strip heat 2 is powered.

All three loads are now powered. To review, they are powered because we closed the thermostat switch, which powered the relay coil, which closed the two relay switches, which allowed power to flow through the three loads.

Are these loads wired in series or are they wired in parallel? We would expect them to be in parallel because we've learned that that for loads to work right, they must be in parallel, not in series. If these loads are in parallel, each of them can get power independently of each other. No series Christmas tree lights here, right? Check it out—

block out just the motor. Could the two other loads be powered if the motor were out? Yes. What if you took out either of the other two loads? Yes, these loads are in parallel.

Ladder diagrams

A ladder diagram is another way to show a circuit. A ladder diagram is intended for troubleshooting, after a system has been installed. When a piece of equipment doesn't work, it's very useful to know where its power is coming from and what switches control it. A connection or hook-up diagram shows us how things wire together. A ladder diagram shows us the logic of how things work together.

A ladder diagram gets its name from its basic framework.

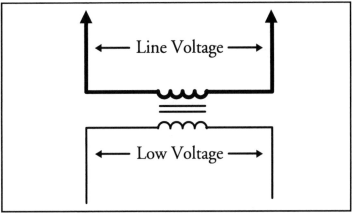

Figure 35. Ladder diagram framework.

Notice a couple familiar things about the ladder diagram framework. In the middle of the ladder diagram is the sym-

bol for the transformer. On the 120V side of the transformer are heavy lines, for line voltage. On the 24V side,
the lines are drawn light.

Using this basic framework, we're going to add *steps* to
the ladder. There will be a step for each load. On that same
step will the switch or switches that control that load.

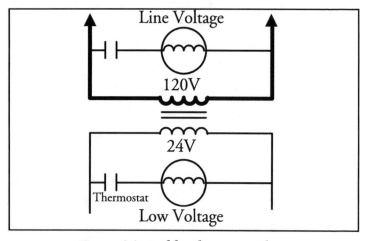

Figure 36. Ladder diagram with *steps*.

The load and switch on the step, plus power supply,
always make a complete circuit. In the diagram above, you
can see that the low voltage load is controlled by the thermostat. It is powered by the 24V side of the transformer.

In the same diagram above, the line voltage step shows
the line voltage load, controlled by a switch, and powered
by line voltage.

We can add loads to either the line or low voltage side

by adding steps. Each step will have one load and at least one switch.

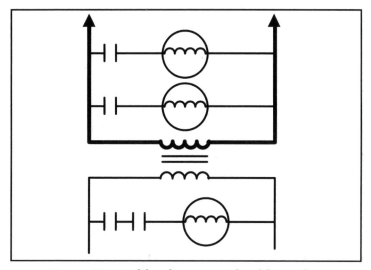

Figure 37. Ladder diagram with additional *steps*.

Notice that the steps of the ladder make lines that are parallel with each other. Interestingly, the loads on each of these parallel lines are parallel loads, so long as they are within the same voltage. Recall the definition of parallel loads. They share a power supply, but operate independently of each other. Use the ladder diagram above to confirm this for yourself.

Notice in the diagram above that the low voltage load is controlled by two switches. These switches are in series. Both switches must be closed for the load to be powered. A ladder diagram is particularly useful for identifying switches in series. You can imagine how frustrating troubleshooting would be if you weren't aware of every switch that could keep a load turned off. Remember, when switches are in series, such as safety switches, it only takes one open switch to disable the load.

Let's look again at the hook-up diagram from a few pages back.

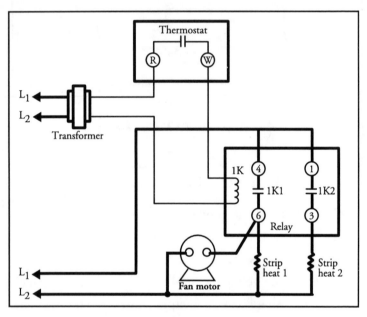

Figure 38. Hook-up diagram.

Here is the ladder diagram of that same circuit.

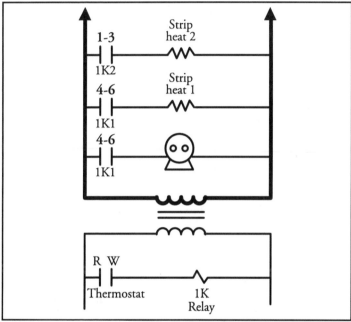

Figure 39. Ladder diagram.

In the hook-up diagram there is one low voltage load. Therefore, we expect to find one step on the 24V side of the ladder diagram. On that step we would find the relay coil (labeled 1K) as the load and the thermostat as the switch. With the 24V side of the transformer as the power supply, we make a complete circuit.

There are three line voltage loads in the hook-up diagram. We would expect to find three steps on the line voltage side of the ladder diagram. There is an individual step for the motor, for strip heat 1, and for strip heat 2. On the step with each load is the switch that controls it. Each load has separate access to the same line voltage power supply. We can see that the loads are in parallel with each other.

Let's look at the step with the motor as the load. What does the ladder diagram tell us about the switch? Because the switch is labeled 1K1, we know this switch is part of a relay. What would it take to close this switch? We would need to power the relay coil. When there is a relay switch, we can expect to find the relay coil in a circuit of another voltage. Look in the low voltage circuit for the the relay coil.

We can see that to power the motor we must close switch 1K1. The only way to close that switch is to power relay coil 1K. Coil 1K is in the 24V circuit. It is powered only when the thermostat is closed. We can see that the low voltage thermostat controls the line voltage motor.

Moving back to the line voltage steps, let's see what powers strip heat 1. Puzzling as it may seem, we see that the switch controlling strip heat 1 is also relay switch 1K1.

Returning to the third step in line voltage, we find strip heat 2 controlled by relay switch 1K2. Once we get used to looking at a ladder diagram, we can see at a glance that relay switches control all three line voltage loads.

Ladder diagrams and hookup diagrams together

Now we're ready to look at an actual diagram that would come with a piece of equipment. First, notice the headings along the top. Here's your first clue that the page contains

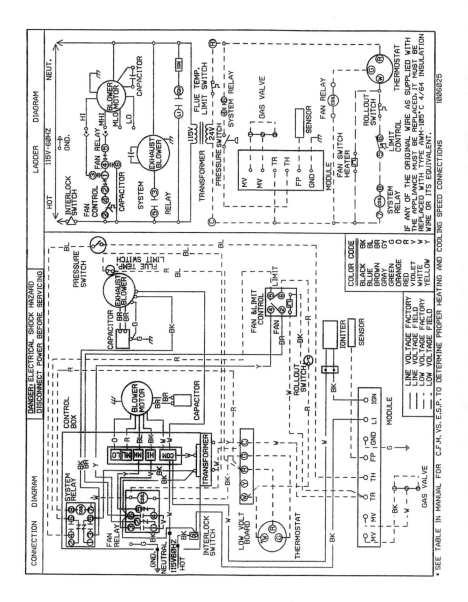

Figure 40. Equipment diagram.

Diagram compliments of Intercity Products.

two separate diagrams, side-by-side. On the left side is the hook-up/connection/schematic diagram (it can be called any of these). On the right is the ladder diagram. Each of the diagrams illustrates the same job. Each diagram takes a different approach to the situation. Depending upon the situation, you would use primarily one or the other.

You would use the connection diagram for original equipment installation. The connection diagram shows exactly what is wired to what. For example, you can see that terminal W on the *thermostat* connects to terminal W on the *low volt board*. You can also see that the two MV terminals on the *module* both connect to the *gas valve*. The dotted lines show that these are low voltage connections.

Use the ladder diagram for troubleshooting once the equipment is installed. You can very quickly identify the loads—there is one load per *step* on the ladder. You also can see what switch controls each load. Perhaps most important of all, you can see if there is more than one switch controlling a load.

Let's concentrate on the ladder diagram and apply some of the many details you've learned.

First, find the transformer near the middle. Notice that the line voltage side (115V) is drawn in solid lines, and the low voltage side (24V) is shown in dotted lines.

On the low voltage side, on the bottom step of the ladder diagram, we find a load labeled *coil* and *system relay*. Because of what we know about relays, we can assume that when this relay coil is powered, one or more switches will change from open to closed, or vice versa. Those switches will be in circuits different from the one that this coil is in. Look elsewhere in the diagram for a *system relay* switch.

A good place to start is on the line voltage side of the transformer. Sure enough, on the second step up from the transformer is a switch labeled *system relay*. It's also labeled with terminals 5 and 3. On that step is a load labeled *exhaust blower*. To power the exhaust blower, we must close the system relay switch.

Still reviewing what we know about relays, what does it take to close this system relay switch? We need to power the system relay coil. And how will we power that coil? Let's look at that coil again (low voltage side, bottom step). We need to close all the switches in that the circuit. How many switches are there? There's the *limit control,* the *roll-out switch,* and the *thermostat.* The first two are already closed. A call for heat will close the thermostat switch between terminals W and R. Is that all the switches? Remember, one of the most powerful functions of the ladder diagram is that it lets us identify all the switches that control a load.

Let's trace the complete circuit for the system relay coil. Starting at the coil, move to the right through the three switches. Continue to trace up toward the transformer (through terminal R) and, oops, there's one more switch-the *flue temp. limit switch.* It's closed. Trace on through the low voltage side of the transformer, and complete the circuit back at the system relay coil. We have a complete circuit. And we know now that there are *four* switches controlling the relay coil.

To look at all this information another way, ask the question, "What does it take to bring on the exhaust blower?" Think: power supply - switch - load. The blower's power supply is the line voltage. The switch is the system relay switch. The load is the exhaust blower. The system relay switch is open—what does it take to close it?

To close the relay switch, we must power the relay coil associated with that switch. We would expect that relay coil to be in a different circuit. We could also expect it to be in a low voltage circuit. We know from having already looked at the diagram that the coil is on the bottom step of the ladder diagram.

We are still tracing backwards to answer the question, "What does it take to power the exhaust blower?" What does it take to power the system relay coil? We must have 24 volts from the transformer. And we must have all four switches closed. All are normally closed except the thermostat. We need a call for heat to close the thermostat.

All of this explanation is the long answer. The short answer-if everything is working right—is that a call for heat brings on the exhaust blower. If everything isn't working, the clues to making it right are in the ladder diagram.

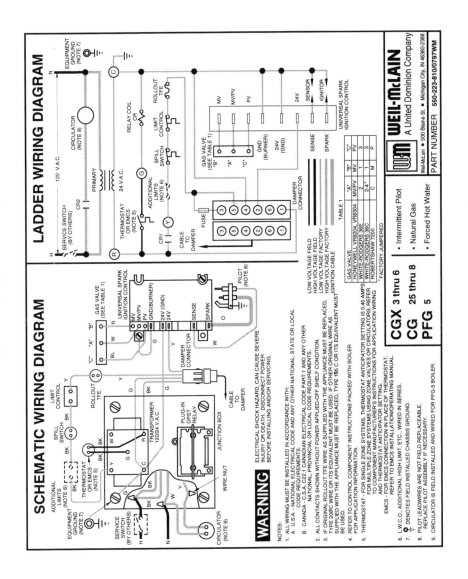

Figure 41. Equipment diagram.

Diagram compliments of Weil-McLain.

Applying Your Knowledge

Now let's apply your knowledge to a new wiring diagram. Use the ladder diagram in Figure 41 to answer these questions. You can find the answers following the questions.

1. In the line voltage circuit, what is the load?

2. In the line voltage circuit, what is the switch?

3. Are there any additional switches?

4. What is the voltage is the power supply of this circuit?

5. In the low voltage circuit, what is the load on the "step" shown closest to the transformer?

6. What is the switch that controls this load?

7. Where would you look to get more details about this switch?

8. What must happen to power this load?
   _____ and_____

9. What happens as a result of relay coil CR being powered?

10. What must happen to close switch CR2?

In the next question, keep in mind that there are internal connections in the universal spark ignition control. Consider the igniter (bottom right) as the load for the series of switches on the bottom low voltage step.

11. On the next "step" down of the low voltage circuit, how many switches are there? (count "additional limits" as one)_____

12. What will it take to close switch CR1?

13. How can you find out what the circled letters R,G,C,Y,W are?

Answers
1. Circulator
2. CR2
3. Service switch (along the side)
4. 120V
5. Relay coil
6. Thermostat
7. Notes in Schematic Wiring Diagram
8. A call for heat to close the thermostat switch, plus 24V from the transformer
9. Switches CR1 and CR2 close.
10. A call for heat, which powers the relay coil
11. Five
12. Power the relay coil
13. Look all over the page. You'll finally find them in the schematic as terminals. No one says this game is fair!

The End

You've made it! You've completed *Quick & Basic Electricity*. You can now look at a ladder diagram and have an idea of where to begin. You probably aren't fast at it yet, but you can get through it.

For those of us who didn't learn electricity and wiring as kids, some of this stuff takes several times through it before it makes any sense. For me it took forever before relays made any sense. If all of this material isn't crystal clear after one time through it, give yourself a pig sticker for being normal and give it another try soon.

And please, feel free to share this book with a friend!

Index

alternating current, 19-20
amp draw, 49
amp rating, 49
amperage, 49-51
anticipator, 52
aquastat, 31

bimetal, 30

circuit
  simple, 17
  series, 34-40
  parallel, 40-43
  open, 27
  closed, 27
comfort, 23
continuity, 48
cph-see cycle rate
cycle rate, 53

diagrams
  hook-up, 61-65, 68, 70-73
  connection, 61-65, 68, 70-73
  schematic, 61-65, 68, 70-73
  wiring, 61-74
  ladder, 65-68, 70-73
  relay, 62
  wiriing, 61
direct current, 19

electromagnetism, 24
electron theory, 15

grounding, 33

humidistat, 29

Kirchoff's Law, 37-40

limit switch, 31
loads, 32-33

mercury bulb, 30
meters, 44
  multimeter, 44
  voltmeter, 46
  ohmmeter, 47-49
  ammeter, 49-51

Ohm's Law, 15
oscilloscope, 19-20

parallel circuits see "circuits"
poles, 28-29
power plant, 20-21
power supply, 18-25

relays, 55-60, 63-64
resistance, measuring, 47-49

series circuits see "circuits"
switches, 26-31
switching action, 31
symbols
  power supply, 22
  switch, 31
  load, 32
  relay, 60
  motor, 32

temperature swing, 54
thermostat, 29-30
  terminals, 63
throws, 28-29
transformer, 20, 24-26
  primary winding, 24-25
  secondary winding, 24-25
  step-down, 23-24
  step-up, 25

VA rating, 51
voltage
  line, 23
  low, 23
voltage, measuring, 45

water analogy, 27
winding
  primary, 25
  secondary, 25

Order Information

To order additional copies of *Quick and Basic Electricity* forward the following information to:

P.I.G. Press
759 E. Phillips Drive S.
Littleton, CO 80122-2673

One copy of *Quick and Basic Electricity* costs $14.95 plus $3.95 for shipping and handling.

Number of books requested: _____

Total Enclosed: _____

Your Name: _____

Your Address (include zip code): _____

_____

_____

Questions? Call P.I.G. Press at:
303-795-2679
or Fax 303-795-9350

Thank you